Let's Target

Vocabulary and Usage

4

D1306734

Araadh

TEACHERS AT WORK

Sadlier School

Let's Target Vocabulary and Usage

Teachers at work™ an imprint of Sadlier School, was created by teachers with teachers in mind to provide the right materials to support students with achieving academic success. Teachers all over the country contributed their ideas and expertise to bring together opportunities for students to practice essential skills and strategies with engaging print and online resources. Together they built a program that will support both teachers and students. We are excited to share these engaging print and online resources with you.

Sadlier School

Cover Series Design: Studio Montage, St. Louis, MO, United States of America

For additional online resources, go to sadlierconnect.com.

William H. Sadlier, Inc.
9 Pine Street
New York, NY 10005-4700

Printed in Singapore.
ISBN: 978-1-4217-4764-4
1 2 3 4 5 6 7 8 9   19 18 17 16 15

PREFACE

Welcome to the *Let's Target*™ Series

Teachers at work™ is excited to introduce this new series to support students in mastering the Common Core State Standards.

The *Let's Target* series was developed by teachers. We understand students need to be engaged in their learning to succeed. With a simple, yet systematic approach, students learn skills and gain confidence to successfully meet the Common Core Standards.

"I got it!" That's what we want students to say when they focus on the lessons in the *Let's Target* series. As teachers, we know how hard it can be to find the right material to boost student achievement. With the *Let's Target* series, students complete the exercises in the book and then go online to reinforce what they have learned.

Want to flip it? Go ahead! Begin with the online resources to jumpstart the learning and then complement the activities with lessons from the book. Either way, students and teachers will be happy to get more opportunities to learn and practice essential skills.

Do you want to work independently or with a peer? *Let's Target* allows for all different kinds of learning strategies. Teachers will find more guidance about this in their Teacher's Guides.

Getting ready for Common Core Assessments? Since the beginning of the Common Core State Standards many have wondered how to prepare students for success. With *Let's Target Vocabulary and Usage*, students will develop vocabulary and move from generalizing and applying it to full vocabulary knowledge and productive use

***Let's Target Vocabulary and Usage* for summer learning?** Students will increase their word knowledge through activities that encourage deep processing of word meanings, figurative language, and word relationships and come back to school ready for success!

Hey Students! Demonstrate your independence in building vocabulary and using it as you read, write, speak, and listen. In this book, you will also learn strategies for acquiring new vocabulary and enhancing communication skills.

The components of the *Let's Target* series include:
- Student Editions with lots of opportunities for **"I got it!"** moments
- Teacher's Guides which support teachers with **CCSS connections** and solutions
- Online Resources give students and teachers the tools to **blend learning** and engage in learning in the classroom and at home

Teachers from around the country collaborated through **Teachers at work** ™, contributing ideas and expertise, to develop this series to prepare students for academic success. Please let us know if you have any ideas that will support students in reaching school success! Contact us at TeachersAtWork@Sadlier.com.

Teachers at work

CONTENTS

Units	Learning Objectives	Exercises	Pages
1 **Antonyms**	• Provide the opposite meaning of another word. • Add prefixes such as 'il', 'im', 'un', 'in', 'ir', 'dis' and 'mis' to form antonyms.	Reading	1
		Exercise 1	2
		Exercise 2	4
2 **Synonyms**	• Provide a word that has the same or nearly the same meaning as another word.	Reading	7
		Exercise 3	8
		Exercise 4	10
3 **Homonyms**	• Understand that homonyms are words that sound the same but are spelled differently and have different meanings. • Learn to use the correct homonym in a sentence.	Reading	13
		Exercise 5	14
		Exercise 6	16
4 **Prefixes**	• A prefix is placed at the beginning of a word to modify or change its meaning. • Use prefixes 're', 'de', 'en' and 'pre' to form words.	Reading	19
		Exercise 7	20
5 **Similes and Metaphors**	• Use similes and metaphors as expressions to describe something by comparing it to something else.	Reading	21
		Exercise 8	22
6 **Idioms**	• Understand that an idiom is a group of words with a meaning of its own that is different from the meaning of each separate word in the idiom. • Use correct idiomatic expressions to convey meaning in context.	Reading	24
		Exercise 9	25
		Exercise 10	27
7 **Word Substitution**	• Replace groups of words without changing their meanings with a single word.	Reading	29
		Exercise 11	30
		Exercise 12	34

Units	Learning Objectives	Exercises	Pages
8 **Compound Words**	• Understand that a compound word is a noun or adjective that is made up of two or more words. • Identify the meaning of the compound through its component words.	Reading	36
		Exercise 13	37
		Exercise 14	39
		Exercise 15	42
		Exercise 16	44
9 **Word Forms**	• Understand that a word can take the form of a verb, noun, adjective or adverb. • Use the word in its various forms in speech and writing.	Reading	46
		Exercise 17	47
		Exercise 18	49
10 **Words Expressing Feelings**	• Use appropriate words to express feelings.	Reading	52
		Exercise 19	53
11 **Phrasal Verbs**	• Understand that a phrasal verb usually consists of a verb and a preposition. • Understand and use the meaning of a phrasal verb in a sentence.	Reading	56
		Exercise 20	57
		Exercise 21	60
12 **Multiple Meaning Words**	• Understand that one word may have more than one meaning, e.g. 'bear', can refer to 'a big furry animal', 'to endure' or 'to give birth'.	Reading	64
		Exercise 22	65
13 **Association**	• Associate a person/thing with another person/thing, e.g. the wings and cockpit are associated with an airplane.	Reading	68
		Exercise 23	69
		Exercise 24	71
14 **Occupations**	• Understand that occupations are jobs that people have and do for a living.	Reading	73
		Exercise 25	74
		Exercise 26	76

SUMMARY NOTES units 1-14   S1-S15

APPENDICES

1. Occupations	(1)1-7
2. Word Forms	(2)1-4
3. Phrasal Verbs	(3)1-8
4. Similes	(4)1-2
5. Idioms	(5)1-5
6. Proverbs	(6)1-4

PERFORMANCE SCORE SHEET

Units	Exercises	Points
1 Antonyms	Exercise 1	☐ / 25
	Exercise 2	☐ / 15
2 Synonyms	Exercise 3	☐ / 20
	Exercise 4	☐ / 15
3 Homonyms	Exercise 5	☐ / 20
	Exercise 6	☐ / 20
4 Prefixes	Exercise 7	☐ / 10
5 Similes and Metaphors	Exercise 8	☐ / 10
6 Idioms	Exercise 9	☐ / 10
	Exercise 10	☐ / 14
7 Word Substitution	Exercise 11	☐ / 15
	Exercise 12	☐ / 15
8 Compound Words	Exercise 13	☐ / 12
	Exercise 14	☐ / 16
	Exercise 15	☐ / 15
	Exercise 16	☐ / 15

9 Word Forms	Exercise 17	☐ / 20
	Exercise 18	☐ / 18
10 Words Expressing Feelings	Exercise 19	☐ / 18
11 Phrasal Verbs	Exercise 20	☐ / 15
	Exercise 21	☐ / 20
12 Multiple Meaning Words	Exercise 22	☐ / 30
13 Association	Exercise 23	☐ / 20
	Exercise 24	☐ / 20
14 Occupations	Exercise 25	☐ / 15
	Exercise 26	☐ / 15

ANTONYMS

Read the passage below.

Just the Opposite!

Wendy and William are identical twins. However, they are exact opposites. William is **timid** and **never** likes to try new things. He is **cowardly**. Wendy is **bold**. She **always** likes to try new things. She is **brave**.

Wendy is a **responsible** person. However, William is an **irresponsible** person who often does not study hard. He is **careless** in his work. Wendy, on the other hand, is **careful**.

The two of them cannot **agree** on anything. They often **disagree** and quarrel with each other.

Note: An **antonym** is a word that is opposite in meaning to another word. An antonym can be formed by adding a **prefix** to the word. Some common prefixes are '**il**', '**im**', '**un**', '**in**', '**ir**', '**dis**' and '**mis**'.

EXERCISE 1

Add a suitable prefix to each of the following words to get its antonym.

1. behave : Misbehave

2. aware : unaware

3. popular : unPopular

4. correct : incorrect

5. human : inhuman

6. belief : disbelief

7. moral : immoral

8. fortune : misfortune

9. logical : illogical

10. known : unknown

✓

11. courtesy : discourtesy

12. legitimate : illegitimate ✓

13. regular : irregular ✓

14. relevant : irrelevant ✓

15. perfect : unperfect ✗

16. mature : inmature ✓

17. spell : misspell ✓

18. sane : insane ✓

19. common : uncommon ✓

20. visible : invisible ✓

21. happy : unhappy ✓

22. action : inaction ✓

23. lawful : unlawful ✓

24. legal : illegal ✓

25. possible : inpossible ✗

EXERCISE 2

Rewrite the following sentences. Change the words in bold to their opposites, by adding suitable prefixes.

1. Jamie's grandparents are **literate**.

   Jamie's grandparents are illiterate.

2. The owner of the house was **aware** of the burglary.

   The owner of the house was unaware of the burglary

3. David is a very **responsible** monitor.

   David is a very irresponsibly monitor.

4. The road is now **passable** to heavy vehicles.

   The road is non impassable

5. Mr. Jones has a rare disease that is **curable**.

   Mr. Jones has a rare disease that is uncurably ✗

6. It is **likely** that all the students will attend the party.

   it is unlikely that all the students ✓

7. Have you **locked** all the doors? ✓

Have you unlocked all the doors

8. Watching television is **allowed** at certain times of the day. ✓

Watching television is allowed at certain times of the day

9. Most of the foreign workers are **skilled**. ✓

most of the foreign workers are unskilled

10. My younger brother is **capable** of looking after himself. ✓

My younger brother is incapable of looking after himself

11. Jack's handwriting is quite **legible**. ✓

Jack's handwriting is quite illegible

12. The principal is talking to the students in the hall. His voice is quite **audible**. ✓

The principal is talking to the students in the hall. His voice is quite inaudible

13. Do you think Susan will **agree** with us? ✓

Do you think Susan will disagree with us

14. His name sounds **familiar** to me.

~~His~~ His name sounds unfamiliar

15. The young robber was **armed**.

The young robber was unarmes

Read the passage below.

Caught in a Sandstorm

The Sahara desert is a **dangerous** place. However, a group of men decided to travel through the desert on camels. It was a **perilous** journey.

When they first started out, there was **scarcely** any wind, so the travellers were able to travel quickly. However, they had **barely** travelled a few miles before strong winds started to blow.

In a distance, they could see **huge** clouds of sand approaching them. They sat on their camels, **dumbfounded**. They did not expect to be caught in the powerful grip of nature and were, therefore, extremely **surprised**.

The men hurriedly put on their airtight goggles. Then they got off their camels and made the animals sit down. They pressed themselves against the leeward side of the camels and braced themselves for the **massive** sandstorm.

> Note: A **synonym** is a word that has the same or nearly the same meaning as another word.

EXERCISE 3

Match the words in table A with their synonyms in table B. The first one has been done for you.

Table A		
1. shorten	**8.** motionless	**15.** wicked
2. assist	**9.** gain	**16.** sad
3. confess	**10.** predict	**17.** edible
4. reduce	**11.** stubborn	**18.** distant
5. bogus	**12.** reluctant	**19.** correct
6. disaster	**13.** appropriate	**20.** attire
7. sickness	**14.** vast	

Table B		
decrease	admit	abbreviate
calamity	help	fake
gloomy	eatable	faraway
accurate	profit	huge
outfit	foretell	obstinate
unwilling	suitable	evil
disease	still	

A	B	A	B
1. shorten	abbreviate	**11.** yard	lawn
2. Qick	fast	**12.** String	yarn
3. desent	ok	**13.** Plane	jet
4. huge	geiente	**14.** happy	joyfull
5. Small	tiny	**15.** mem orall	momentes
6. energe	power	**16.** Sport cantest	olimpics
7. aqua	water	**17.** game	sport
8. flame	fire	**18.** angry	mad
9. table	dresck	**19.** PJ's	night
10. atom	fall	**20.** hill	montan

EXERCISE 4

Rewrite the following sentences replacing the words in bold with suitable synonyms from the box.

suddenly	renowned	angry	allowed
selected	behavior	polite	fierce
foe	force	eager	hidden
errors	predict	hate	

1. The teacher is **cross** with Jim whose work is always so untidy.

   The teacher is angry with Jim whose work is is always so untidy

2. Gary is **keen** to take part in the concert.

   Gary is eager to take part in the concert

3. We should learn to be more **courteous** to one another.

   We should learn to be more polite to one another

4. The show ended **abruptly**.

   The show ended suddenly

5. Is Albert a friend or an **enemy**?

Is Albert a friend or an unfriendly person

6. The postman was attacked by a **ferocious** dog.

the postman was attucked bya fierce dug

7. The **famous** singer was mobbed by her fans.

The Poular singer was mobbed X by her fahs

8. There are many spelling **mistakes** in his composition.

there are many spellig errors in his composition

9. Tom's **conduct** has improved since the counseling session.

10. Don't **compel** her to go if she doesn't want to join us.

Don't force her to go if she doesn't wnant to join us

11. No one is **permitted** to leave the class during the examination.

No one was permitted to leave the class

12. Where has the thief **concealed** the stolen goods? ✓

Where has the thief hided the
stolen

13. Only the best players will be **chosen** to represent the school. ✗

Only the best palayers will be
picked to represent

14. No one can **foretell** what is going to happen in the future.

No one can perdit what is going to happen
in the future ✓

15. I **detest** people with bad manners.

I dislike people with bad manners ✗

HOMONYMS

Read the passage below.

Lost in the Woods

The ground was **bare** except for a few leaves. John was frightened that he would run into a **bear**. He walked carefully and kept a lookout for growling sounds. He had to **bow** his head to go under a low tree branch. Seeing a **bough** on the ground, he stepped over it quietly. Then he stopped to listen.

At that moment, he saw an eagle **soar** into the air. John was so stunned that he stumbled over a rock and fell. His arms and knees were **sore**.

John sat on the ground. He felt very **weak**. It had been only two days but it felt like it had been a **week**. He bowed his head and clasped his hands together to **pray**. He hoped he would not fall **prey** to any wild creatures before help arrived.

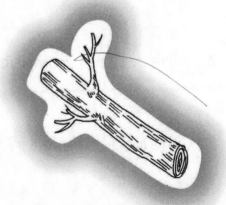

Then he thought he heard faint voices in a distance calling his name. Was he dreaming? The voices grew louder. John mustered his strength and shouted back. He was finally saved!

Note: **Homonyms** are words which sound the same but are spelled differently and have different meanings. The five homonyms here are 'bough' and 'bow', 'bare' and 'bear', 'soar' and 'sore', 'weak' and 'week' and, 'pray' and 'prey'. More examples include 'hole' and 'whole', 'made' and 'maid', 'key' and 'quay', 'idle' and 'idol', and so on.

EXERCISE 5

Choose the correct word and fill in each blank.

1. The wound will take some time to _heal_.
(heel / heal)

2. Climbing the highest mountain in the world is a remarkable _feat_.
(feet / feat)

3. Mr. Benson is the _sole_ breadwinner of the family.
(sole / soul)

4. A good teacher can be a _role_ model for the students.
(roll / role)

5. It took the police only ten minutes to arrive at the _scene_ of the crime.
(seen / scene)

6. The robber was nabbed by some members of the public before he could _flee_.
(flee / flea)

7. The lifeguard tried in _vain_ to save the drowning girl.
(vain / vein)

8. The tourist told the taxi driver to take the shortest _route_ to the airport.
(root / route)

9. Some workers were injured at the construction _site_.
(site / sight)

10. Mary is not beautiful. In fact, she is rather _Plain_. ✓

(plane / plain)

11. A polar bear has thick, white _fur_. (fir / fur) ✓

12. Jimmy is not going to school today. He has the _flu_. ✓

(flew / flu)

13. I shouted until my voice went _hoarse_, but Andy still did ✓
not hear me.

(hoarse / horse)

14. Of _course_ I will help Jim. After all, he is my good friend. ✓

(coarse / course)

15. The referee sent the player out because of _foul_ ✓
play.

(fowl / foul)

16. The doctor gave the patient an injection to _lessen_ his ✓
pain.

(lessen / lesson)

17. James does not want to talk. He has a _sore_ throat ✓
today.

(soar / sore)

18. Lawrence won a gold _Medal_ in the sporting event. ✓

(medal / meddle)

19. The lion _preys_ on the deer. (prays / preys) ✓

20. The emperor's _fein_ lasted only two years. ✗

(rein / reign)

EXERCISE 6

Fill in each blank with a suitable word.

> pedals   peddles

1. Mary _Peddly_ her wares by going from house to house.

2. Linda has a new tricycle but her legs are not long enough to reach the _Peduls_.

> find   fined

3. The lost child could not _find_ his way home.

4. In many countries, people are _fined_ for spitting and littering.

> minor   miner

5. The _miner_ was seriously injured by an underground explosion in the coal mine.

6. The culprit, who was a _minor_, was let off with a stern warning. ✓

main	mane

7. The _____Mane_____ of a lion makes it look majestic. ✓

8. The _____main_____ reason for his failure is laziness. ✓

sow	sew

9. The farmers _____sow_____ their seeds in the springtime. ✓

10. Not too long ago, mothers used to _____sew_____ clothes for their children. ✓

stationary	stationery

11. The driver was hurt when his car crashed into a _____stationary_____ truck. ✓

12. I am going to write to Frank. I need some _____stationery_____. ✓

> weather   whether

13. It has been raining the whole day. I hope the _Weather_ will be fine tomorrow.

14. I am not sure _Whether_ Jane will attend the party tonight.

> site   sight

15. The construction _site_ is breeding mosquitoes.

16. The setting sun is indeed a beautiful _sight_!

> leek   leak

17. Water is seeping out. There is a _leak_ in the tank.

18. Some people do not like the taste of _leek_.

> root   route

19. Let's take the shortest _route_ to our destination.

20. The _root_ of the ginseng plant is believed to have medicinal properties.

PREFIXES

Read the passage below.

Jeremy **enjoyed** going for long rides in his father's car. He would drive along the expressway and Jeremy would be able to see the beautiful countryside on one side and the ocean on the other. Sometimes, Jeremy would **pretend** to drive the car as well.

Once, his father took a **detour** while he was on the expressway. He took Jeremy down a long and winding road. There were many colorful flowers on both sides of the road.

Jeremy could not wait for the next summer holidays. His father had promised to take him for another long drive.

A prefix is placed at the beginning of a word to modify or change its meaning. It cannot stand alone. Some common prefixes are 're', 'de', 'en' and 'pre'.

Fill in the blanks with words that start with the prefixes 'pre', 'en', 're' or 'de'.

Refer to *Summary Notes: Unit 4* for help.

1. To save the forests, you should _recycle_ this stack of papers instead of throwing them away.

2. Could you please _enlarge_ this picture? It is much too small.

3. The triceratops is a _prehistoric_ animal that lived during the Late Crateceous period.

4. King Thomas was a tyrant who was _defeated_ by his brother. His brother became the next king.

5. The mountaineers will _endanger_ their lives by continuing their hike in the stormy weather.

6. The movie _preview_ tells you what the movie is about and whether the movie is worth watching.

7. The chef had to _catch_ the fish before cooking it. He used a knife to remove all the bones.

8. My five-year-old sister is still in _preschool_ and not in elementary school.

9. Can you _encrypt_ this secret message? It's full of signs and symbols.

10. You have to _retake_ the Math test if you do not pass.

SIMILES AND METAPHORS

Read the passage below.

Mr. and Mrs. Thomson have two children. Mr. Thomson is **as industrious as a beaver**. He works very hard to support his family.

Their children, Jacky and Tracy, are very different in looks and character. Jacky is a messy and disorganized person. His room is **a disaster area**. He prefers to watch television at home to playing outdoor games. When his favorite show is on, he will be **glued to his seat**.

Tracy, although younger than Jacky, is bigger in size. She is **as lively as a cricket** and is always playing games. Unlike Jacky, she is **as playful as a kitten** and she loves playing tricks on others. She often plays tricks on Jacky too.

EXERCISE 8

Fill in the blanks with the correct similes from the box.

butter fingers	like a fish out of water
two peas in a pod	as red as a cherry
as fit as a fiddle	as gentle as a lamb
as dark as a dungeon	as poor as a church mouse
like a hungry wolf	a heart of stone

1. Ben, who lives in the city, felt _butter fingers_ when he spent a week at his uncle's farm.

2. As there was no electricity, the house was _as gentle as a lamb_ once night fell.

3. Hannah certainly has _as fit pod_. She keeps dropping things.

4. Anna and Maria are like _two peas in pod_. They have the same hobbies and they enjoy doing many things together.

5. Her nose was _as red as cherry_ when she came in from the cold.

6. The king has _a heart_ (of stone). He will not give any money to help the poor in his kingdom.

7. Although my grandfather is ninety years old, he is _as fit as a fiddle_. He even takes part in marathons.

8. The nanny was _as gentle_ when she took care of the infant.

9. That man is _as poor_ (as a church mouse). He does not even have money for a simple meal.

10. Ken ate _like a hungry wolf_ and gobbled down his food in minutes.

Read the passage below.

Painfully Sweet

Sue always **had a sweet tooth**. She liked to eat chocolates, sweets and cakes. One night, she was **burning the midnight oil** to prepare for her examinations. As she studied, she kept shoving jellybeans into her mouth.

A few weeks later, she had a toothache. To avoid getting a scolding, she told her mother **a cock and bull story** about how she got her toothache. However, her mother knew that she was not telling the truth. She has fully aware of Sue's weakness for sweets and chocolates.

The next day, Sue's mother took her to the dentist. Sue's mother told her **to bear in mind** the consequences of eating too many sweets. True enough, the doctor recommended extracting a badly decayed tooth. Sue had learned a lesson. She decided to **turn over a new leaf**.

> Note: An **idiom** is a group of words with a meaning of its own that is different from the meaning of each separate word in the idiom. The English language is full of **idiomatic expressions**.

EXERCISE 9

Complete the idioms in the following sentences.

Refer to *Appendix 5: Idioms* for help.

1.  They had to stay indoors as it was **raining** <u>cats and dogs</u>.

2.  Henry was **building** <u>castles in the air</u> when the teacher called him.

3.  The clown **pulled** <u>out the stop</u> to make the people laugh.

4.  The dog **turned** <u>rogue</u> when I tried to hold its leash.

5.  The farmer certainly **has** <u>a green thumb</u> His plants grow very well.

6.  Please **lend** me _a hand_. The box is too heavy.

7.  You have to speak loudly as the old man is **hard** _of hearing_.

8.  Kenneth is very fond of **blowing** _blowing her. own trupit_

9.  The robber **took** _flite_ when he saw the police.

10.  The hunter was terrified when he came **face** _to face_ with a tiger.

EXERCISE 10

Complete the following sentences with suitable idioms from the given box.

a white lie	make a mountain out of a molehill
a greenhorn	at the eleventh hour
an old hand	in the nick of time
face the music	learning it by heart
at my fingertips	turn over a new leaf
a cock and bull story	save for a rainy day
once in a blue moon	footing the bill

1. Mr. Davies is _an old hand y n eart_ in the food business. He lacks experience.

2. Mr. Lawrence is _n the eleven t._ He is giving us a treat.

3. Mr. Terry is _an old hand nour_ in the company. He has a lot of experience.

4. I know the facts thoroughly. They are _at my fingertips_ _____.

5. The students are trying to memorize the poem. They are _learning it by_ _____ for the performance. _heart_

6. "You must finish your project early and not _in th_
   the nick," said the teacher.
        ○ time

7. You are telling me _a   white lie_. I do not
   believe you at all.

8. The boy almost drowned and was saved _in the_
   nick of time

9. After much counseling by the teacher, the boy decided to
   turn over a new and study hard.
        leaf

10. The family of eight must be thrifty. They go for meals in
    restaurants _ant my fin yer tips_

11. James realized his wrongdoing and was prepared to
    face the music.

12. In order to protect his younger brother, Ben told his parents
    a white lie.

13. It is a good habit to spend wisely and _save for a_
    _____.   _rainy day_

14. The matter is not as serious as he says. I think he is trying to
    make   a   mountain   out of
        _a_
    molehill

WORD SUBSTITUTION

Read the passage below.

A Familiar Face in Oak Street

Those who live near Oak Street or travel that route frequently would be familiar with a beggar who always sits at the end of the street.

Some say that he is **blind**, but others do not believe that he **cannot see**. They think that he is only pretending to be blind. He is **skinny**. Since he looks **very thin**, he looks like he **does not have enough food to eat**. He only collects a **meager** amount of food every day. The **small amount** that he collects means that he is probably **starving**.

Sometimes, someone would buy a fast food meal or a loaf of bread and pass it to the beggar. He would thank the kind soul **again and again**. It can become a little embarrassing especially when the beggar thanks the person **repeatedly**. It is comforting to know that the people who live near Oak Street are helpful and look out for one another.

Note: From the words in bold in the passage, we can see that the words '**blind**', '**skinny**', '**meager**', '**starving**' and '**repeatedly**' can replace groups of words without changing their meanings.

EXERCISE 11

For each of the following sentences, choose the answer which could be replaced by the word in bold.

1. The **audience** cheered when the actor appeared on the stage.

   (1) people in the hall
   (2) people watching the show
   (3) people talking in the hall
   (4) people acting on the stage

2. The twins were finally reunited after a **decade**.

   (1) period of ten days
   (2) period of ten weeks
   (3) period of ten months
   (4) period of ten years

3. There was **panic** among the hotel guests when the fire broke out.

   (1) sudden great joy
   (2) sudden great fear
   (3) sudden excitement
   (4) sudden sorrow

4. The principal is **addressing** the students in the hall.

   (1) making a speech to
   (2) shouting loudly at
   (3) scolding
   (4) discussing with

5. The **famine** caused great hardship to the poor villagers.

(1) scarcity of water
(2) scarcity of food
(3) scarcity of money
(4) scarcity of fuel

6. The teacher reminded the students not to **omit** the punctuation marks in their composition.

(1) add to
(2) leave out
(3) write out
(4) put in

7. The house is surrounded by huge trees and is **invisible** from the road.

(1) cannot be touched
(2) cannot be reached
(3) cannot be seen
(4) cannot be occupied

8. Many of the small islands in the Pacific Ocean are **uninhabited**.

(1) not forested
(2) not cultivated
(3) not developed
(4) not populated

9. The prisoners were **executed** at dawn.

   (1) put to death
   (2) sent to another prison
   (3) sent to work
   (4) set free

10. Susan **screamed** when she was bitten by a snake.

   (1) cried out in pain
   (2) gave a loud, sharp cry
   (3) shouted excitedly
   (4) cried loudly

11. The crowd **ignored** the victim's cry for help.

   (1) paid full attention to
   (2) paid no attention to
   (3) listened carefully to
   (4) heard clearly

12. The house was **burglarized** yesterday.

   (1) broken into by thieves
   (2) destroyed by fire
   (3) pulled down
   (4) rented out

13. The plan has to be carried out **immediately**.

   (1) without preparation
   (2) without consideration
   (3) without help
   (4) without delay

14. Smuggling and drug use are **illegal** in most countries.

    (1) not allowed by customs

    (2) not allowed by the law

    (3) not allowed in schools

    (4) not allowed by parents

15. The teacher **regretted** losing her temper in class.

    (1) felt sorry for

    (2) felt happy for

    (3) felt relieved for

    (4) felt good for

Fill in the blanks with the correct words from the box.

feeble	continuously	audible	apologized
distant	annoying	notorious	promoted
meager	illegible	infallible	sympathize
mob	century	immortal	

1. Rosie's voice is not **loud enough**. It is hardly _audible_.

2. The gangster, Peter, is **well-known but in a bad way**. He is _notorious_.

3. The beggar is **old and weak**. He is _feeble_.

4. It has been raining **without stopping** for two hours. It has been raining _continuously_.

5. The fortune-teller said he **could never make mistakes**. He claimed to be _infallible_.

6. Mark **said sorry** to his friends for being late. He _apologized_ to them.

7. Alaska seems to be so **far away** from our state. It seems so _distant_.

8. Stop **making** me **angry**. Stop _annoying_ me.

9. Ben's father has been **given a higher post** in the company.
   He has been _promoted_

10. The unskilled worker is earning a **very small** salary. His salary
    is _meager_.

11. The police dispersed the **noisy and angry crowd**. The
    mob was dispersed by the police.

12. Tom's handwriting is **difficult to read**. His handwriting is really
    illegible

13. The ancient statue took more than **a hundred years** to build.
    It took more than a _century_ to build.

14. No one can **live forever**. No human being is _immortal_.

15. I really **feel sorry** for the refugees. I _sympathize_ with their
    fate.

COMPOUND WORDS

● ● ●

Read the passage below.

A Rainy Day Plan

Sam tapped his **keyboard** many times, but nothing appeared on the screen. He paced about in his **bedroom**. There was a **thunderstorm** outside, so there was nothing to do. He wanted to play **football** or **baseball** with his friends, but he could not.

An hour later, Sam's friend rang the **doorbell**. Sam was surprised to see his friend in a **raincoat** with a **waterproof** bag on his back. He had a grin on his face. He told Sam that he was going to explore the **man-made waterfall** at the park. Since the **downpour** had now become a drizzle, Sam agreed to go.

Sam grabbed a few necessities and threw them into his **backpack**. He put on a raincoat and wore his **outdoor footwear**. Then he locked the main door and gate before joining his friend.

Note: A **compound word** is a noun or an adjective that is made up of two or more words. Usually, the meaning of the **compound word** is closely related to the meaning of its component words. For example, the adjective '**man-made**' means that something is artificial or made by man. Some examples of compound nouns are fireman, seafood, warehouse, underpass, etc. Some examples of compound adjectives are self-taught, short-lived, ill-mannered, undernourished, etc.

EXERCISE 13

Match each of the words in table A with a suitable word in table B to form a compound noun. The first one has been done for you.

Table A		
1. dust	5. sun	9. match
2. star	6. stop	10. hand
3. foot	7. fire	11. lamp
4. head	8. toad	12. camp

Table B		
scarf	works	glasses
fire	fish	shade
stool	box	bag
over	bin	print

Table A	Table B	Compound word
1. dust	bin	dustbin
2. Star	fish	starffish
3. foot	s	
4.		
5.		
6.		
7.		
8.		
9.		
10.		
11.		
12.		

EXERCISE 14

Look at the pictures and fill in the missing half of each of the compound nouns.

1.

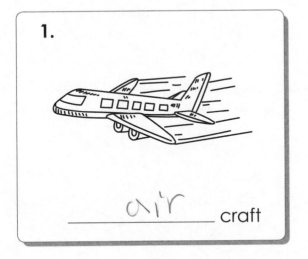

_____ air _____ craft

2.

_____ mail _____ man

3.

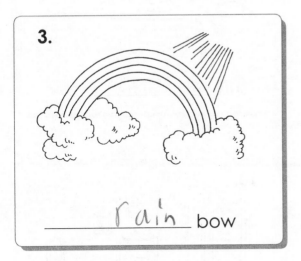

_____ rain _____ bow

4.

_____ snow _____ hill

5.

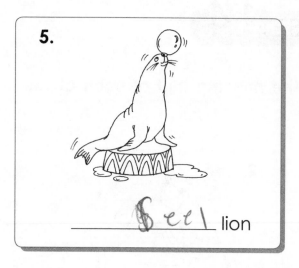

_____ Seel lion

6.

_____ hair dresser

7.

_____ bad fruit

8.

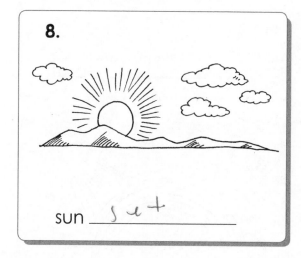

sun _____ set

9.

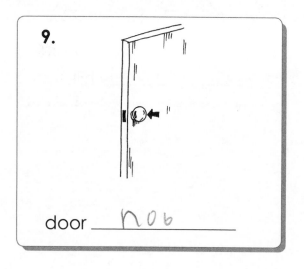

door _____ nob

10.

bed _____ room

11.

hand _shack_

12.

news _paper_

13.

water _melon_

14.

fire _fly_

15.

fire _fiter_

16.

sea _path_

Join each of the words in Table A with a suitable word in Table B to form a compound adjective. The first one has been done for you.

Table A		
1. war	6. tight	11. self-
2. straight	7. second	12. full-
3. up	8. well-	13. ill-
4. water	9. soft-	14. under
5. cold-	10. blue-	15. over

Table B		
conscious	set	boiled
like	proof	behaved
collar	forward	blooded
grown	fisted	hand
active	mannered	developed

	Table A	Table B	Compound word
1.	war	like	warlike
2.			
3.			
4.			
5.			
6.			
7.			
8.			
9.			
10.			
11.			
12.			
13.			
14.			
15.			

EXERCISE 16

Fill in the blanks with the correct words in the given box.

accident-prone	secondhand	underpaid	well-built
well-balanced	cold-hearted	overactive	top-class
well-mannered	waterproof	self-taught	upright
home-cooked	handmade	well-to-do	

1. The champion boxer is a/an _____ man with big muscles.

2. How can you be so _cold heart_? Don't you have any pity for the poor starving children?

3. There are many _hand made_ hotels in New York City.

4. Mr. Smith may be poor, but he is certainly a/an _self taugh_ man.

5. Alex has never attended any music school. In fact, he is a/an _____ musician.

6. Jason comes to school in a big car. He comes from a/an _____ family.

7. The _____ car Mark bought last week is giving him a lot of trouble.

8. Regular exercise and a/an _____ diet will keep you healthy.

9. Mother always says _____ food is the best.

10. The motorist slowed down as he approached the _____ area.

11. We like our class monitor because he is helpful and _____.

12. Some people say that _____ breads taste better than those made by machine.

13. The workers are unhappy because they are _____.

14. That child simply cannot keep still. He is _____.

15. Umbrellas are made of _____ fabric.

Read the passage below.

A Discussion in Class

Mrs. Smith could feel her students' eyes on her. For once, they were all paying **attention**. They had never been so **attentive** before. One of them had asked her a question. However, she did not know the answer. She could not **decide** whether to tell them the truth or to change subjects. She had to make a **decision** soon.

Just then, Annie, one of her students, raised her hand. "I know the answer," she said **proudly**. Mrs Smith heaved a sigh of relief and beamed with **pride** at Annie.

Annie tried to **explain** how she derived the answer. Her **explanation** was, however, very confusing. Noticing the time, Mrs. Smith hurriedly concluded the lesson and told her students to try and solve it at home. She would also take the chance to discuss it with her colleagues.

Note: A word can take the form of a **verb, noun, adjective** or **adverb.**

Fill in the blanks with the correct form of the words in brackets.

Refer to *Appendix 2: Word Forms* for examples.

1. The warm and humid weather yesterday made me feel very
   _____.   (sleep)

2. Everybody likes Ann as she is such a _____ person.
                                                           (help)

3. Sean is an honest and _____ boy. You can count
   on him when you need help.   (depend)

4. The students decorated the stage _____.
                                                           (creative)

5. The victim could not give a clear _____ of the robber
   to the police.   (describe)

6. Jim is always _____ despite being poor. (cheer)

7. My grandfather has been very _____ lately.
                                                           (forget)

8. The goods are _____ displayed in the shop.
                                                           (attract)

9. Use your _____ and write a story about a world
   without electricity.   (imagine)

10. After a hard day's work, Mr. Lee is now resting _____
    in his armchair.   (comfort)

11. Cigarette smoke is _____ to our health. (*harm*)

12. Terrence is becoming more and more _____. His parents simply cannot control him. (*rebel*)

13. Susan's house was _____ decorated with antiques. (*beautiful*)

14. To ease traffic congestion, the road has to be _____. (*wide*)

15. The man's unusual behavior aroused the policeman's _____. (*suspect*)

16. The student has not been attending class regularly. He is _____ not interested in his studies. (*simple*)

17. "Must I always be _____ to my parents?" the student asked the teacher. (*obey*)

18. 'Fat people are lazy' is an extremely _____ remark. (*offend*)

19. It may sound incredible, but I think his story is _____. (*believe*)

20. The house was _____ entered when the owner was fast asleep. (*force*)

EXERCISE 18

Fill in the blanks with the correct words.

sleep	sleeps	sleepy	sleepily

1. Tom walked _____ to the kitchen in the middle of the night.

2. The newborn baby needs a lot of _____.

3. The man is feeling _____ after a heavy meal.

4. My grandfather _____ only five to six hours a day.

succeed	success	successful	successfully

5. If you want to _____, you must work hard.

6. The project was _____ completed.

7. _____ never comes easy.

8. John's uncle is a _____ businessman.

danger	dangerous	dangerously

9. The house is in _____ of being swept away by the floodwater.

10. The motorist was fined for driving _____.

11. It is extremely _____ to catch a cobra with your bare hands.

destroyed	destruction	destructive	destructively

12. The volcanic eruption caused serious _____ to the village.

13. The school was completely _____ by the fire.

14. The _____ power of an earthquake is indeed terrifying.

15. The typhoon is blowing _____ across the country.

able	ability	ably

16. The manager is _____ assisted by his secretary.

17. None of the students were _____ to answer the question.

18. You do not need any special _____ to do the job.

WORDS EXPRESSING FEELINGS

Read the passage below.

Rediscovering the Joys of Family Relationships

Mark was **terrified** about hiking in the mountains. He was **worried** that he might meet with wild animals. His sister found it **amusing** when he told her about his fears. She called him names. Mark was **annoyed** with his sister for laughing at him. He was **determined** to hike in the mountains. Feeling **sorry** for him, Mark's sister offered to go hiking with him.

On the day of the hike, Mark and his sister headed towards the mountains. It had been a long time since they had done things together. They were pleasantly **surprised** that they had so many things to talk about. When they reached the top of the mountain, they were **overwhelmed** with awe at the scenery below them. They stood there, **breathless**.

As they made their way downhill, the two siblings agreed that they should do a monthly hike together.

Note: The words in bold express **feelings**.

EXERCISE 19

Choose the correct answers and fill in the blanks.

1. David felt extremely _____ staying at home all
   alone the whole day.　　　　　(*boring / bored / shocked*)

2. We were _____ when we heard the good news
   last night.　　　　(*shocked / disappointed / overjoyed*)

3. His offensive remark _____ me.
   　　　　　　　　　　　(*angered / encouraged / excited*)

4. I find it _____ that some people actually litter in
   elevators.　　　　(*enchanting / disgusting / thrilling*)

5. The residents _____ when the fire broke out.
   　　　　　　　　　　(*panicked / worried / despaired*)

6. "I _____ liars and selfish people," said Derrick.
   　　　　　　　　　　　　　　(*admire / like / detest*)

7. After quarreling with her good friend, Mary, Jane felt
   _____.　　　　　　(*happy / funny / miserable*)

8. We should not _____ a person just because he is
   ugly or poor.　　　　　　(*admire / love / despise*)

9. Francis has just lost his job and he has no money. He feels
_____. (desperate / lonely / shocked)

10. The principal is _____ of the students' academic
achievements. (gloomy / unhappy / proud)

11. The tourists from the United States viewed the Great Wall of
China with _____. (disgust / awe / sadness)

12. James is _____ for all the help his friends have given
him. (fearful / delightful / grateful)

13. Mr. Johnson never _____ helping a person.
(regrets / fears / worries)

14. After the operation, the patient feels _____.
(lonely / bored / weak)

15. Mrs. Rogers was _____ when she discovered that
her son had been lying to her.
(delighted / dismayed / sorry)

16. Jack felt _____ when he failed the driving test the
third time. (hopeless / hopeful / excited)

17. The lazy worker is _____ that he might be dismissed by his employer.   (angry / afraid / excited)

18. Mrs. Ramsey was _____ when her son did not return home for dinner. She feared that something might have happened to him.   (worried / irritated / furious)

PHRASAL VERBS

Read the passage below.

War

A fierce battle was taking place. Suddenly, a bomb **went off**. Team A had **blown up** Team B's fort. However, Team B refused to **give in**. They did not **give up** trying to destroy Team A's fort as well. The fighting **carried on**. The battle **came about** because both teams were fighting to gain control of the country.

If only both teams had taken the time and effort to **sit down** and **talk out** the problems that were affecting their country, a war could have been avoided.

> Note: A **phrasal verb** usually consists of a verb and a preposition. It is used as a single verb but with a new meaning.

Complete the phrasal verbs in the following sentences.

Refer to *Appendix 3: Phrasal Verbs* to complete the sentences.

1.  This antique vase is not easy to **come**

   _____.

2.  When Jim **came** _____, he found himself in the hospital.

3.  Adrian has eaten too much and is now **throwing** _____.

4.  Last night, a large crowd **turned** _____ for the show.

5.  Last month, Dawn's grandfather **passed** _____ after a long illness.

6.  Carol did not answer when the teacher **called** _____ her name because she was daydreaming.

7.  Thieves **broke** _____ the house when the owner was sleeping.

8.  The boy needed help, but the people around him just **looked** _____ helplessly.

9.  I am not sure how the accident **came** _____.

10.  The doctor advised Mr. Max to **give** _____ smoking.

11.  What do the stars in the United States flag **stand** _____?

12.  The volunteers are **giving** _____ food baskets to the senior citizens.

13.  It took the firefighters an hour to **put** _____ the fire.

14.  The toy **gave** _____ a loud piercing sound when the boy stepped on it.

15.  The students just **carried** _____ talking despite the teacher's stern warning.

EXERCISE 21

Rewrite the following sentences. Replace the phrasal verbs.

Refer to *Appendix 3: Phrasal Verbs* for help.

1. The guards were sleeping when the prisoners **broke out**.

   _____

   _____

2. The VIP was **called upon** to give away the prizes.

   _____

   _____

3. The match had to be **put off** because of bad weather.

   _____

   _____

4. The two friends **broke up** after a quarrel.

   _____

   _____

5. The students were told to **keep up** their good results.

   _____

   _____

6. The teacher **handed out** some sweets to the students.

   _____

   _____

7. The manager will **look into** the workers' complaints.

_____

_____

8. I am still trying to **figure out** why Bernard has become so unfriendly.

_____

_____

9. The teacher told the students to **go ahead** with their project.

_____

_____

10. The unemployed man is desperately **looking for** a job.

_____

_____

11. Many people are willing to spend a lot of money **doing up** their apartments.

_____

_____

12. Tiffany's mom **put up** her drawing on the refrigerator.

_____

_____

13. The tourists have never **come across** a guide quite like Stella.

_____

_____

14. Frank is rather weak in English. He is determined to **catch up with** the rest of the class.

_____

_____

15. Do you think platform shoes will **catch on** in our country?

_____

_____

16. Most parents and teachers today are not in favor of **doing away with** examinations.

_____

_____

17. I **look upon** Gordon as a friend and a brother.

_____

_____

18. The people **look up to** their honest and capable leaders.

_____

_____

19. The soldiers are expected to **carry out** all their duties promptly.

_____

_____

20. I am going to the birthday party. Would you like to **go with** me?

_____

_____

MULTIPLE MEANING WORDS

Read the passage below.

A Change of Luck

A **bear** wounded a young boy. Unable to **bear** the pain any longer, the boy passed out in the middle of the forest. An elderly lady walked by and saw the boy. She hurriedly took him home and nursed him back to health. As she was unable to **bear** any children, she treated the boy like her son and hoped that he could live with her.

When the boy learned of the elderly lady's intention to adopt him, he was close to tears. A case of ill luck had turned into something good for him. He had found himself a home.

> Note: The English language contains many **words which have more than one meaning**. In the story above, the word 'bear' can refer to a 'big furry animal', 'to endure' or 'to give birth'.

Fill in the blanks with the correct words from the given box. You have to use each word twice.

arms	break	mine	book	bow
cross	lie	flat	fire	last
safe	fly	land	sow	lead

1. The workers are having their coffee _____.

2. It is a Japanese custom to greet each other with a _____.

3. The brave soldier was only armed with a _____ and ten arrows.

4. Please handle the vase with care. Do not _____ it.

5. The coal _____ was closed last year after two serious accidents.

6. The boss decided to _____ the lazy worker.

7. Terrance lives in a bungalow but his friend lives in a _____.

8. His _____ and face were swollen after he was stung by bees.

9. This mobile phone belongs to me. It is _____.

10. Timothy ran very fast in the race but he still came in _____.

11. The firefighters finally put out the _____.

12. This pair of shoes will not _____ you a year.

13. George was pushed from behind and he fell _____ on his face.

14. America is the largest _____ exporter.

15. The customer complained that there was a _____ in her soup.

16. The _____ is a Christian symbol.

17. Mrs. Owen kept all her expensive jewelry in the _____.

18. The plane from China is going to _____ at London Airport soon.

19. Some large birds, like the ostrich, cannot _____.

20. The teacher was _____ with Nancy for daydreaming in class.

21. It is always not _____ to open your door to strangers.

22. Most of the _____ in the mountainous country is rocky and infertile.

23. _____ is used in the making of waterpipes.

24. Spring is the best time for the farmer to _____ his seeds.

25. 'Around the World in Eighty Days' is an interesting _____. Many students have read it.

26. The doctor told the patient to _____ on the examination bed.

27. We have to _____ the tickets for the musical in advance.

28. Mrs. Smith is angry with her son for telling her a _____.

29. The _____ has just given birth to ten piglets.

30. David volunteered to _____ the police to the scene of the crime.

Read the passage below.

Physical Exercises

Several activities were going on in the hall at the same time. Brandon and Shawn had their **rackets** and **shuttlecock**. They were ready to play **badminton**. Over at the other end of the hall were Ben and Peter. They had their **rackets** and **balls**, ready to play a game of **tennis**.

In the field, a game of **baseball** was going on. Jim was ready to hit the **ball** with his **bat**. He wondered if he could run to the first **base** before the ball was caught.

It was definitely a very busy day in school for the students.

Note: When we see a **racket** and a **shuttlecock**, we **associate** them with **badminton**. Similarly, we would **associate tusks** and a **trunk** with an **elephant**, a **baton** and **handcuffs** with the **police**, **doctors** and **patients** with a **hospital**, **caddies** and **clubs** with **golf**, **goggles**, **flippers** and **oxygen tanks** with **diving**, and so on.

EXERCISE 23

For each of the following words in the box, underline two words in the brackets that are associated with it.

1. **mosquito** (malaria food honey blood desert)

2. **doctor** (awl stethoscope medicine duster wealth)

3. **Eskimo** (seal kayak horse forest wigwam)

4. **fish** (arms paddle scales fins beef)

5. **shirt** (tie ribbon sleeves collar hat)

6. **sun** (heat crescent beach rays figs)

7. **desert** (trees rivers sand camels fish)

8. **boot** (heel sleeve sole sponge handle)

9. **bed** (carpet mattress rubber blanket seat)

10. **bee** (disease honey bread sting sugar)

11. **knife** (blade paint handle vegetable meat)

12. bicycle (engine gasoline water spokes pedals)

13. panda (China Mexico meat bamboo disease)

14. cobbler (brush anvil cloth awl shoes)

15. ship (deck bridge hood hand pet)

16. soccer (linesmen shooters arrows rackets goalkeeper)

17. window (knob curtain grill pillow wood)

18. kettle (saucer wood lid spout basket)

19. cobra (coconut poison fangs food handbag)

20. mortuary (crops corpse heat cold wind)

EXERCISE 24

With what do we associate the following pairs of words? Fill in the blanks with the words in the box.

book	airplane	computer	horse
flower	blacksmith	clock	bear
rifle	confectionery	bird	door
crab	chimney	pastor	king
tree	postman	pants	Eskimo

1. mouse, monitor : _____

2. petals, stigma : _____

3. anvil, hammer : _____

4. letters, packages : _____

5. crown, throne : _____

6. saddle, mane : _____

7. wings, cockpit : _____

8. face, hands : _____

9. barrel, trigger : _____

10. cub, fur : _____

11. pincers, shell : _____

12. pastries, cakes : _____

13. author, cover : _____

14. hinges, knob : _____

15. ice, igloo : _____

16. branch, trunk : _____

17. wings, feathers : _____

18. pulpit, sermon : _____

19. zip, pockets : _____

20. soot, smoke : _____

Read the passage below.

Occupations

Mr. Brown, the **baker**, kneaded, braided, and decorated the loaf of whole wheat bread. Then he placed it in the display case. At that very moment, the oven bell sounded. Mr. Brown took out a tray of bread from the oven. It smelled delicious.

Mr. Brown had just put all the bread in the display case when his first customer came into the shop. It was Mrs. Smith. She was a **hairdresser**. She was very popular as she was good at cutting hair. She also helped to wash and style people's hair.

Soon, Mr. Brown's shop was bustling with customers.

Note: A person's **occupation** is the job that he or she does for a living.

EXERCISE 25

Fill in the boxes with the missing letters.

Refer to *Appendix 1: Occupations* for definitions of vocabulary words.

1. The **s __ __ g __ __ n** decided to operate on the patient at once.

2. The **g __ __ __ m** cleans the stable and bathes the horses every day.

3. The **l __ __ b __ __ j __ __ __** is cutting down a huge tree.

4. The smugglers in the speedboat are trying hard to evade the **c __ __ __ tg __ __ __ d.**

5. Andy is an **e __ tr __ __ ren __ __ r**. He owns several hotels in the United States and Canada.

6. Mary is listening attentively to the **p __ __ __ __ r** delivering a sermon.

7. The audience really enjoyed the funny acts of the **c __ __ __ n.**

8. The **j __ __ k __ __** fell from his horse towards the end of the race.

9. His mother is a **se __ __ __ s __ r __ __ s**. She can sew ten dresses a day.

10. Mr. Hansen is an **ad** _ _ _ _ **l**. He commands a fleet of warships.

11. Anna is a successful **w** _ _ _ _ **r**. She has written a number of books.

12. Mrs. Smith is attending a party tonight. She needs a **b** _ _ **ys** _ _ _ _ **r** to take care of her child.

13. The **m** _ **g** _ _ **i** _ **n** pulled a rabbit out from his hat.

14. The **c** _ **s** _ _ _ **r** is busy serving the customers at the checkout.

15. The water pipe is leaking. Send for the **pl** _ _ **b** _ _.

EXERCISE 26

Underline the correct answers.

1. Gina performs daring gymnastic stunts in the circus. She is a/an (stuntwoman / acrobat / clown).

2. Dr. Cohen looks after children and treats their illnesses. He is a (surgeon / specialist / pediatrician).

3. Mr. Clifford digs up and studies historical remains. He is a/an (archaeologist / historian / philanthropist).

4. John's uncle investigates crimes and goes after criminals. He is a (lawyer / detective / prosecutor).

5. James is a (chef / butler / chauffeur). He drives his employer to the office every day.

6. Susan is a/an (maid / adviser / counselor). She is helping the delinquent student turn over a new leaf.

7. Tina reports news and writes articles for the newspaper. She is a (journalist / finalist / specialist).

8. Mr. Cox is a (mason / chef / curator). He is in charge of the National Museum.

9. Mr. Sam studies the stars and predicts future events. He is an (astrologer / astronaut / astronomer).

10. Mrs. Lester's job is to help people find suitable partners to marry. She is a (controller / governor / matchmaker).

11. Joe's father is a (ranger / shepherd / warden). His job is to take care of sheep.

12. Mr. Davies is a (foreman / manager / peon). He supervises a group of workers at the construction site.

13. Andrew is a (caterer / provider / server). He provides food and drinks at a party.

14. Mr. Lee is a (trader / dealer / manager). He buys and sells goods for a profit.

15. Alice's job is to serve the passengers on board an airplane. She is a (waitress / stewardess / servant).

Vocabulary and Usage

SUMMARY NOTES

TEACHERS AT WORK

Sadlier School

UNIT 1

A Antonyms

An antonym is a word that is opposite in meaning to another word. Some antonyms can be formed by adding prefixes such as 'il', 'im', 'un', 'in', 'ir', 'dis' and 'mis'.

B Examples

bold	—	timid
brave	—	cowardly
increase	—	decrease
selfish	—	generous

C Antonyms Beginning With A Prefix

(A) Adding prefix 'il'

legal	—	illegal
legible	—	illegible
legitimate	—	illegitimate
literate	—	illiterate
logical	—	illogical

(B) Adding prefix 'im'

mature	—	immature
moral	—	immoral
passable	—	impassable
perfect	—	imperfect
possible	—	impossible

(C) Adding prefix 'un'

armed	—	unarmed
aware	—	unaware
common	—	uncommon
familiar	—	unfamiliar
known	—	unknown
lawful	—	unlawful
likely	—	unlikely
locked	—	unlocked
popular	—	unpopular
skilled	—	unskilled

(D) Adding prefix 'in'

audible	—	inaudible
capable	—	incapable
correct	—	incorrect
curable	—	incurable
human	—	inhuman
sane	—	insane
visible	—	invisible

(E) Adding prefix 'ir'

regular	—	irregular
relevant	—	irrelevant
responsible	—	irresponsible

(F) Adding prefix 'dis'

agree	—	disagree
allowed	—	disallowed
belief	—	disbelief
courtesy	—	discourtesy

(G) Adding prefix 'mis'

behave	—	misbehave
fortune	—	misfortune
spell	—	misspell

UNIT 2

(A) Synonyms

A synonym is a word that has the same or nearly the same meaning as another word.

(B) Examples

abruptly	—	suddenly	bogus	—	fake
appropriate	—	suitable	chosen	—	selected
assist	—	help	compel	—	force
attire	—	dress	concealed	—	hidden

conduct	—	behavior	keen	—	eager
confess	—	admit	mistakes	—	errors
correct	—	accurate	motionless	—	still
courteous	—	polite	permitted	—	allowed
cross	—	angry	predict	—	foretell
dangerous	—	perilous	reduce	—	decrease
disaster	—	calamity	reluctant	—	unwilling
distant	—	faraway	sad	—	gloomy
edible	—	eatable	scarcely	—	hardly
famous	—	renowned	shorten	—	abbreviate
ferocious	—	fierce	sickness	—	disease
foe	—	enemy	stubborn	—	obstinate
gain	—	profit	vast	—	huge
hate	—	detest	wicked	—	evil

UNIT 3

A Homonyms

Homonyms are words which sound the same but are spelt differently and have different meanings.

B Some Common Homonyms

bear	—	bare	flew	—	flu
bough	—	bow	fowl	—	foul
coarse	—	course	fur	—	fir
current	—	currant	heel	—	heal
feet	—	feat	hoarse	—	horse
find	—	fined	hole	—	whole
flee	—	flea	idle	—	idol

key	—	quay	roll	—	role
leek	—	leak	root	—	route
lessen	—	lesson	seen	—	scene
made	—	maid	site	—	sight
main	—	mane	soar	—	sore
medal	—	meddle	sole	—	soul
minor	—	miner	sow	—	sew
peddle	—	pedal	stationary	—	stationery
plane	—	plain	vain	—	vein
prays	—	preys	weak	—	week
rein	—	reign	weather	—	whether

UNIT 4

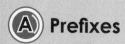 **Prefixes**

A prefix is a group of letters that can be added to a word to change the meaning of the word.

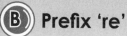 **Prefix 're'**

recycle
retake
review

 Prefix 'en'

endanger
enlarge

Prefix 'pre'

prehistoric
preschool

 Prefix 'de'

debone
decode
dethroned

 UNIT **5**

 People

A simile is an expression that is used to describe something by comparing it to something else using 'like' or 'as'. A metaphor is an expression that is used to describe something by making comparisons between it and something else.

 Examples

a disaster area	as playful as a kitten
a heart of stone	as poor as a church mouse
as dark as a dungeon	as red as a cherry
as fit as a fiddle	butter fingers
as gentle as a lamb	like a fish out of water
as industrious a a beaver	like a hungry wolf
as lively as a cricket	two peas in a pod

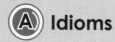

UNIT 6

(A) Idioms

An idiom is a group of words with a meaning of its own that is different from the meaning of each separate word in the idiom.

Refer to Appendix 5: Idioms

UNIT 7

(A) Word Substitution

A single word can replace a group of words without changing the meaning.

(B) Examples

addressing	: making a speech to	**century**	: a hundred years
annoying	: making (someone) angry	**continuously**	: without stopping
apologized	: said sorry	**decade**	: period of ten years
audible	: loud enough	**distant**	: far away
audience	: people watching the show	**executed**	: put to death
		famine	: scarcity of food
blind	: cannot see	**feeble**	: old and weak
burglarized	: broken into by thieves	**ignored**	: paid no attention to

illegal	:	not allowed by the law	**omit**	: leave out
illegible	:	difficult to read	**panic**	: sudden great fear
immediately	:	without delay	**promoted**	: given a higher post
immortal	:	live forever	**regretted**	: felt sorry
infallible	:	could never make mistakes	**repeatedly**	: again and again
			screamed	: gave a loud, sharp cry
invisible	:	cannot be seen	**skinny**	: very thin
meagre	:	very small	**starving**	: do not have enough food to eat
mob	:	noisy and angry crowd		
			sympathize	: feel sorry
notorious	:	well-known but in a bad way	**uninhabited**	: not populated

UNIT 8

 A **Compound Words**

A compound word is a noun or an adjective that is made up of two or more words.

Usually, the meaning of the compound word is closely related to the meaning of its component words.

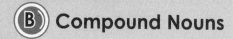

B Compound Nouns

aircraft	matchstick
baseball	newsstand
bedroom	postman
campfire	rainbow
doorbell	raincoat
doorknob	sandpaper
downpour	seafood
dustbin	sealion
firefly	seashore
fireman	seaside
fireworks	starfish
football	starfruit
foothill	stopover
footprint	sunglasses
hairdresser	sunrise
handbag	thunderstorm
handphone	toadstool
handshake	underpass
headmaster	underwear
headscarf	warehouse
keyboard	waterfall
lampshade	watermelon
matchbox	waterworks

Compound Adjectives

accident-prone	straightforward
bad-tempered	tightfisted
blue-collar	top-class
cold-blooded	underdeveloped
cold-hearted	undernourished
full-grown	underpaid
half-baked	upright
handmade	upset
home-cooked	warlike
ill-mannered	waterproof
man-made	watertight
overactive	well-balanced
secondhand	well-behaved
self-conscious	well-built
self-taught	well-mannered
short-lived	well-to-do
soft-boiled	

UNIT 9

 Word Forms

A word can take the form of a verb, noun, adjective or adverb.

Refer to Appendix 2: Word Forms

UNIT 10

(A) Words Expressing Feelings

We use certain words when we want to express our feelings.

(B) Examples

afraid	grateful
amusing	hopeless
angered	miserable
annoyed	overjoyed
awe	overwhelmed
bored	panicked
breathless	proud
desperate	regrets
despise	sorry
determined	surprised
detest	terrified
disgusted	weak
dismayed	worried
furious	

UNIT 11

(A) Phrasal Verbs

A phrasal verb usually consists of a verb followed by a preposition. It is used as a single verb but with a new meaning.

Refer to Appendix 3: Phrasal Verb

UNIT 12

(A) Multiple Meaning Words

The English language contains many words which have more than one meaning.

(B) Examples

- **arms**
  - (a) the two long parts of your body between your shoulders and hands
  - (b) weapons used for fighting a war

- **bear**
  - (a) a big furry animal
  - (b) endure
  - (c) give birth

- **book**
  - (a) a set of pages that have been fastened together inside a cover to be read
  - (b) to make arrangements to go to a theater, eat at a restaurant, etc. at a particular day and time

- **bow**
  - (a) the act of bending your body forward to show respect to someone
  - (b) a type of weapon used with arrows

- **break**
  - (a) a short period of time to rest or eat
  - (b) to damage something

- **cross**
  - (a) an object in the shape of a cross used as a symbol of Christianity
  - (b) annoyed or angry

- **fire**
  - (a) the state of burning something that produces flames and smoke
  - (b) to remove someone from a job

- **flat**
  - (a) to fall in such a way that you are lying on your chest on the ground
  - (b) a room that is part of a larger building

- **fly**
  - (a) a type of insect
  - (b) the movement made by birds or insects when they move through the air using their wings

- **land**
  - (a) ground
  - (b) to arrive at a place in a boat, airplane, etc.

- **last**
  - (a) after everyone else
  - (b) to remain in good condition after a period of time

- **lead**
  - (a) to take someone somewhere by getting him to follow you
  - (b) a type of metal

- **lie**
  - (a) something that you say or write that is untrue
  - (b) to be in a position where your body is flat on a surface

- **safe**
  - (a) not in danger
  - (b) a strong metal box with special locks to keep your money or jewelry in

- **sow**
  - (a) a female pig
  - (b) to plant seeds in the ground

A Association

To associate one person / thing with another is to make a mental connection between one person / thing with another.

B Persons / Things That Are Often Associated With One Another

airplane	— wings, cockpit	boot	— heel, sole
badminton	— racket, shuttlecock	chimney	— soot, smoke
baseball	— ball, bat, base	clock	— face, hands
bear	— cub, fur	cobbler	— awl, shoes
bed	— mattress, blanket	cobra	— poison, fangs
bee	— honey, sting	computer	— mouse, monitor
bicycle	— spokes, pedals	confectionery	— pastries, cakes
bird	— wings, feathers	crab	— pincers, shell
blacksmith	— anvil, hammer	desert	— sand, camels
book	— author, cover		

diving	— goggles, flippers, oxygen tank	mortuary	— corpse, cold
doctor	— stethoscope, medicine	mosquito	— malaria, blood
		panda	— China, bamboo
door	— hinges, knob	pants	— zip, pockets
elephant	— tusks, trunk	pastor	— pulpit, sermon
Eskimo	— ice, igloo, seal, kayak	postman	— letters, parcels
		rifle	— barrel, trigger
fish	— scales, fins	ship	— deck, bridge
flower	— petals, stigma	shirt	— sleeves, collar
golf	— caddie, clubs	soccer	— linesmen, goalkeeper
horse	— saddle, mane		
hospital	— doctors, patients	sun	— heat, rays
		tennis	— racket, ball
Japan	— sushi, judo	tree	— branch, trunk
kettle	— lid, spout	war	— bombs, tanks, guns
king	— crown, throne		
knife	— blade, handle	window	— curtain, grill

 UNIT 14

(A) Occupations

A person's occupation is what he or she does for a living.

Refer to Appendix 1: Occupations for a list of occupations and their descriptions.

Vocabulary and Usage

APPENDICES

APPENDICES

The Appendices are designed as a cross grade level reference tool that can be used in writing, preparing discussions and presentations, and in building vocabulary.

1: OCCUPATIONS

A

accountant	one who keeps a record of the money received or sent
acrobat	one who does daring acts at a circus
admiral	one who commands a fleet of warships
adviser	one who gives advice, typically someone who is expert in a particular field
apprentice	one who is attached to someone to learn a skill or trade
archaeologist	one who studies ancient societies by examining buildings, tools of people who lived in the past, etc.
architect	one who designs buildings
astrologer	one who foretells events by studying the stars
astronomer	one who studies the stars
author	one who writes books

B

babysitter	one who takes care of a baby while his parents are out and is paid to do this
baker	one who bakes and sells bread, cakes, pastries, etc.
banker	one who owns, manages or has a share in the control of a bank
barber	one who cuts hair for men
bartender	one who mixes and serves drinks at a bar, pub or hotel
beautician	one who gives beauty treatment to a person's skin, hair, etc.
biologist	one who studies or works in the study of living things
blacksmith	one who makes things from iron
bodyguard	one who guards and protects an important person
bricklayer	one who builds walls, buildings, etc. with bricks

	butcher	one who kills animals, cuts them up and sells their body parts
	butler	(male) one who is the main servant of a house
C	caddie	one who carries golf clubs, picks up the golf balls, etc. for a golf player
	caretaker	one who looks after a building
	carpenter	one who makes wooden objects, especially furniture
	cartoonist	one who draws cartoons
	cashier	one who collects or pays out money in a bank, shop, restaurant, etc.
	caterer	one who provides food and drinks at an event
	chauffeur	one who drives someone's car
	chef	an experienced or main cook in a hotel or restaurant
	choreographer	one who arranges how dancers should move in a performance
	cleaner	one who cleans people's houses, offices, etc.
	clerk	one who is employed to do filing of records, photocopy letters, keep accounts in office, etc.
	clown	one who entertains people in a circus
	coastguard	one who helps to prevent illegal activities from taking place around the coast
	cobbler	one who mends shoes
	composer	one who writes music
	conductor	one who directs an orchestra or a choir
	confectioner	one who makes or sells cakes, pastries, etc.
	contractor	one who agrees to furnish materials or to do a piece of work for a certain price
	coroner	one who finds out the cause of a person's death
	counselor	one who is trained to listen to people and give them advice about their problems
	curator	one who is in charge of a museum or an art gallery
D	dentist	one who examines and treats people's teeth
	detective	one who finds information that will lead to the criminals being caught
	diplomat	one who is an official representing one's own country in another
	director	one who controls or manages a company
	doctor	one who treats sick people
	draftsman	one who draws plans of buildings

E	editor	one who prepares a book, magazine or newspaper for printing
	electrician	one who makes, installs or repairs electrical appliances
	engineer	one who designs and makes machines, bridges, etc.
	engraver	one who cuts or carves on metal, wood, steel, etc.
	executioner	one who kills a criminal (especially legally as a punishment)
	explorer	one who travels to little-known lands or seas to learn more about them
F	farmer	one who owns or manages a farm
	fishmonger	one who buys and sells fish
	florist	one who sells flowers
	foreman	one who is in charge of and watches over a group of workers
G	gamekeeper	one who breeds and protects wild animals and birds
	gardener	one who grows and tends to plants in a garden
	geographer	one who studies the mountains, seas, climate and population in the world
	geologist	one who studies the soil and rocks that form the Earth
	goldsmith	one who makes and sells things made of gold
	greengrocer	one who sells vegetables and fruit
	grocer	one who sells dry food and preserved food as well as other household products
	groom	one who takes care of horses
H	hairdresser	one who cuts and perms hair for women
	herbalist	one who studies, collects, sells or administers herbs as medicine
	historian	one who writes recorded events of the past as a book
	housekeeper	one who manages a household and its affairs
I	interpreter	one who translates what one person says to another, especially when they speak different languages so that they can understand each other
	inventor	one who produces something new

J

jeweler	one who deals in or makes jewelry
jockey	one who rides horses in races
journalist	one who writes or produces articles for a newspaper or magazine
judge	one who hears and decides cases in a law court

L

laborer	one who does strenuous work which involves little skill
lawyer	one who gives advice about matters of law or acts for others in a court
librarian	one who is in charge of books in a library
locksmith	one who makes and mends locks
lumberjack	one who cuts down trees for wood

M

machinist	one who operates a machine
maid	one who does cleaning work in a house or hotel
magician	one who performs tricks for entertainment
magistrate	one who is empowered to apply and enforce the law
manager	one who controls or takes charge of a business, hotel, etc.
mason	one who cuts and prepares stone or brick for building
matchmaker	one who arranges marriages or romantic relationships between people
mechanic	one who repairs machinery
midwife	one who is trained to help women when they are giving birth
miller	one who owns a mill or works on it to grind grain into flour
milliner	one who makes, trims and sells women's hats
money-changer	one who buys and sells currencies for profit
moneylender	one who lends money to people who pay the money back with interest

N

navigator	one who directs the course of a ship or an aircraft
newsagent	one who delivers or sells newspapers
newsreader	one who reads the news on radio or television
novelist	one who writes long stories
nurse	one who is trained to take care of the sick; a person who takes care of and brings up babies for others

O	optician	one who makes or sells eye glasses and other optical instruments
	organist	one who plays the organ
	overseer / foreman	one who supervises a group of workers
P	pediatrician	one who looks after children and treats their illnesses
	pastor	one who is a leader in a church
	pathologist	one who studies the causes and effects of illnesses
	peddler	one who goes from house to house selling things
	peon	one who does odd jobs and runs errands
	pharmacist	one who is qualified to compound and sell drugs
	photographer	one who takes photographs for a newspaper, magazine, film studio or an individual
	physician	one who has the general skills of a medical doctor but is not a surgeon
	pianist	one who plays the piano
	pilot	one who flies an aircraft
	plasterer	one who covers the walls and ceilings with plaster
	playwright / dramatist	one who writes plays or drama
	plumber	one who repairs pipes and fixtures in buildings
	poacher	one who hunts or fishes in private territory without permission
	poet	one who composes poems
	policeman	one who maintains law and order
	potter	one who makes earthenware from baked clay by hands
	postman	one who delivers mail and parcels
	professor	one who is a teacher and is of the highest rank in a department of a university
	programmer	one who produces computer programs
	psychiatrist	one who is trained as a doctor and specializes in the study of mental illnesses
R	referee	one who is a judge of a game
S	salesman	one who sells goods
	scavenger	one who searches for things among unwanted objects
	sculptor	one who carves or models figures from wood, metal, stone, clay, etc.

	seamstress	one who sews and makes clothes
	secretary	one who writes letters, keeps records and manages the office of a company or club
	sentry / sentinel	one who keeps watch outside a building and gives warning of danger
	shepherd	one who takes care of sheep
	stenographer	one who is skilled in writing in shorthand
	steward / stewardess	one who attends to the needs of passengers on a ship or aircraft
	stockbroker	one who buys and sells stocks or shares on behalf of his clients
	stunt man / stunt woman	one who is employed to take the place of an actor or actress when doing something dangerous in a film
	supervisor	one who makes sure that things are done the correct way
	surgeon	one who studied medicine and performs operations
	surveyor	one who measures and records details of areas of land
T	tailor	one who makes clothes
	tanner	one who makes animal skin into leather by tanning
	taxidermist	one who fills the skins of dead animals with special material so that they look like they were alive
	therapist	one who is trained to give a particular type of treatment for physical or mental illness
	tour guide	one who takes travelers to visit places of interest
	trader	one who buys and sells goods for a profit
	treasurer	one who takes charge of collected funds
	typist	one who types letters, memos, reports, etc. in an office
U	umpire	one who ensures that a game is played fairly and in an orderly manner
	undertaker	one who arranges funerals
V	vendor	one who sells goods
	veterinarian	one who is an expert in treating the diseases of animals
	violinist	one who plays the violin

W	waiter / waitress	one who serves food and drinks at the table in a restaurant
	warden	one who takes charge of a prison or jail
	watchmaker	one who makes and mends watches
	welder	one who joins pieces of metal using heat or high pressure
	writer	one who writes books or articles to be published
Z	zoologist	one who is an expert in the study of animal life

2: WORD FORMS

	Verb	Noun	Adjective	Adverb
A	—	ability	able	ably
	abuse	abuse	abusive	abusively
	—	accident	accidental	accidentally
	admire	admiration	admirable	admirably
	advertise	advertisement	—	—
	—	—	agreeable	agreeably
	agree	agreement	agreed	—
	amuse	amusement	amusing	amusingly
	anger	anger	angry	angrily
	announce	announcement	—	—
	appoint	—	appointed	—
	attend	attendance	—	—
	attend	attention	attentive	attentively
	attract	attraction	attractive	attractively
	arrive	arrival	—	—
B	beautify	beauty	beautiful	beautifully
	behave	behavior	behavioral	behaviorally
	believe	belief	believable	—
	benefit	beneficial	—	—
	boast	boastfulness	boastful	boastfully
	brave	bravery	brave	bravely
	broaden	—	broad	broadly
C	—	care	careful	carefully
	—	care	careless	carelessly
	cheapen	cheapness	cheap	cheaply
	cheer	cheerfulness	cheerful	cheerfully
	choose	choice	chosen	—
	color	color	colorful	colorfully
	—	comfort	comfortable	comfortably
	comfort	comfort	—	—
	compare	comparison	comparative	comparatively
	compete	competition	competitive	competitively
	consider	consideration	considered	—
	corner	corner	—	—
	—	courage	courageous	courageously
	create	creativity	creative	creatively
	criticize	criticism	critical	critically

	Verb	Noun	Adjective	Adverb
D	—	danger	dangerous	dangerously
	—	decisiveness	decisive	decisively
	decide	decision	—	—
	decorate	decoration	decorative	decoratively
	—	defensiveness	defensive	defensively
	defend	defense	—	—
	delight	delight	delighted	delightedly
	delight	delight	delightful	delightfully
	depend	dependence	dependent	dependently
	describe	description	descriptive	descriptively
	despair	despair	despairing	despairingly
	destroy	destruction	destructive	destructively
	die	death	dead	—
	disappoint	disappointment	disappointed	disappointedly
	disgust	disgust	disgusted	—
	disgust	disgust	disgusting	disgustingly
	dread	dread	dreadful	dreadfully
E	ease	easiness	easy	easily
	encourage	encouragement	encouraging	encouragingly
	enjoy	enjoyment	enjoyable	enjoyably
	equalize	equality	equal	equally
	—	—	excited	excitedly
	excite	excitement	exciting	excitingly
	exceed	excess	excessive	excessively
	—	excellence	excellent	excellently
	expect	expectation	expectant	expectantly
	explain	explanation	explanatory	—
	express	expression	expressive	expressively
	extend	extension	extensive	extensively
F	fancy	fancy	fanciful	fancifully
	favor	favor	favorable	favorably
	—	foolishness	foolish	foolishly
	force	force	forceful	forcefully
	forget	forgetfulness	forgetful	forgetfully
	—	fortune	fortunate	fortunately
	free	freedom	free	freely
	frighten	fright	frightened	—
	frighten	fright	frightening	frighteningly
H	—	happiness	happy	happily
	—	harmlessness	harmless	harmlessly
	harm	harm	harmful	harmfully

Verb	Noun	Adjective	Adverb
hate	hatred	hated	—
help	helpfulness	helpful	helpfully
—	honesty	honest	honestly
hunger	hunger	hungry	hungrily
hurry	hurry	hurried	hurriedly

I

Verb	Noun	Adjective	Adverb
idle	idleness	idle	idly
ignore	ignorance	ignorant	ignorantly
imagine	imagination	imaginative	imaginatively
imitate	imitation	imitative	—
—	peril	perilous	perilously
impress	—	impressive	impressively
improve	improvement	—	—
infect	infection	infectious	infectiously
insist	insistence	insistent	insistently
intend	intention	intentional	intentionally

K

Verb	Noun	Adjective	Adverb
know	knowledge	knowledgeable	knowledgeably

L

Verb	Noun	Adjective	Adverb
laze	laziness	lazy	lazily
lighten	—	—	—
loosen	looseness	loose	loosely

M

Verb	Noun	Adjective	Adverb
—	mischief	mischievous	mischievously
—	misery	miserable	miserably

N

Verb	Noun	Adjective	Adverb
neglect	neglect	neglectful	neglectfully
—	nervousness	nervous	nervously

O

Verb	Noun	Adjective	Adverb
obey	obedience	obedient	obediently
oblige	—	obliging	obligingly
offend	offense	offensive	offensively
originate	origin	original	originally

P

Verb	Noun	Adjective	Adverb
—	peacefulness	peaceful	peacefully
perform	performance	performing	—
—	peril	perilous	perilously
persist	persistence	persistent	persistently
persuade	persuasion	persuasive	persuasively
pity	pity	pitiful	pitifully
poison	poison	poisonous	poisonously
predict	prediction	predictable	predictably
presume	presumptuousness	presumptuous	presumptuously
—	pride	proud	proudly
produce	—	productive	productively

Verb	Noun	Adjective	Adverb
—	—	prohibitive	prohibitively
prohibit	prohibition	—	—
promote	promotion	promotional	—
prosper	prosperity	prosperous	prosperously
R			
—	reasonableness	reasonable	reasonably
reason	reason	reasoned	—
rebel	rebellion	rebellious	rebelliously
regret	regret	regrettable	regrettably
—	reliability	reliable	reliably
rely	reliance	reliant	—
relieve	relief	relieved	—
repeat	repetition	repeated	repeatedly
repent	repentance	repentant	—
resent	resentment	resentful	resentfully
S			
sadden	sadness	sad	sadly
satisfy	—	satisfactory	satisfactorily
satisfy	satisfaction	satisfying	satisfyingly
secure	security	secure	securely
select	selectivity	selective	selectively
shame	shamefulness	shameful	shamefully
silence	silence	silent	silently
simplify	simplification	simple	simply
—	sleepiness	sleepy	sleepily
—	softness	soft	—
starve	starvation	starved	—
succeed	success	successful	successfully
—	—	suspicious	suspiciously
suspect	suspicion	suspected	—
T			
terrify	terror	terrified	—
terrify	terror	terrifying	terrifyingly
—	thoughtfulness	thoughtful	thoughtfully
think	thought	—	—
threaten	threat	threatening	threateningly
tolerate	tolerance	tolerant	tolerantly
trick	trick	tricky	—
W			
widen	width	wide	—

3: PHRASAL VERBS

Phrasal Verb	Meaning(s)
A add to	increase
add up to	(i) give a result
	(ii) become a certain amount
answer to	take orders from or obey someone
ask for	request
ask out	invite someone to go out to a place such as a cinema or a restaurant
B back away	retreat
back off	move backwards
back out	withdraw
back up	support
bargain for	expect
barge in	interrupt rudely
believe in	(i) have trust or confidence in
	(ii) feel sure of the value or worth of
blow up	(i) inflate
	(ii) become very angry
	(iii) explode
break down	(i) collapse
	(ii) become useless, to fail to function or to stop working properly
	(iii) be overcome by emotion and start to cry
break in	interrupt
break into	enter a house or place by force
break off	(i) stop talking suddenly
	(ii) separate
	(iii) end a relationship
break out	(i) escape
	(ii) start to happen
break up	end a relationship
bring about	cause to happen
bring forward	advance
bring up	(i) raise, educate
	(ii) introduce, mention
bring out	(i) develop, publish
	(ii) show clearly

Phrasal Verb	Meaning(s)

C

Phrasal Verb	Meaning(s)
call for	demand
call off	cancel or stop something
call on	pay a short visit
call out	(i) say out aloud
	(ii) summon (to an emergency)
call up	(i) make something appear
	(ii) summon for (military, etc.) service
call upon	invite
carry on	continue
carry out	fulfill or accomplish
catch on	(i) finally understand
	(ii) become popular
catch up with	reach the same standard
check in	register at a hotel
check out	leave a hotel
check up	examine
clear out	(i) leave
	(ii) empty (so as to clean)
clear up	(i) explain something
	(ii) put in order
coat with	cover something with a thin layer of something else
come about	happen
come across	find or meet by chance
come along with	accompany
come back	return to a particular place or person
come by	obtain
come round	regain consciousness
come to	regain consciousness
come up	(i) happen
	(ii) move towards someone
come up with	suggest an idea
cook up	invent (a story)
cry out	shout loudly
cut down	reduce
cut off	(i) stop
	(ii) isolate
	(iii) interrupt
	(iv) disconnect
cut up	slice

D

Phrasal Verb	Meaning(s)
die away	become gradually weaker before stopping
die down	become less strong

Phrasal Verb	Meaning(s)
die out	become extinct
do away with	(i) get rid of
	(ii) kill
do over	do something again
do up	(i) repair
	(ii) fasten
	(iii) renovate
	(iv) improve
doze off	fall asleep
draw back	(i) step back
	(ii) show unwillingness
drive at	mean
drive out	expel
drop in	visit somebody
drop out	withdraw

E
end up	finally be at a particular place

F
face up to	accept the fact
fall apart	break
fall back	move back suddenly from someone
fall behind	fail to do something
fall for	be tricked
fall in with	accept a plan
fall off	become fewer or less
fall out	have a quarrel with someone
fall through	fail
fall upon	suddenly attack
fed up with	feel annoyed
fend off	defend oneself against someone
find out	discover the truth
figure out	understand

G
get ahead	succeed
get around	information or news that is told to a lot of people
get at	criticize
get away with	escape
get into	be involved in something
get off	leave a vehicle like a train or a bus
get on	(i) go onto a vehicle like a train or a bus
	(ii) make progress
get over	(i) recover from
	(ii) finish doing something difficult

Phrasal Verb	Meaning(s)
get round	(i) persuade
	(ii) evade
get through	(i) arrive
	(ii) succeed in speaking to someone on the telephone
give away	(i) make known or reveal
	(ii) distribute freely
give in	surrender
give off	emit
give out	(i) announce
	(ii) be exhausted
	(iii) send out
give up	(i) surrender
	(ii) lose hope
	(iii) stop doing something
go against	oppose
go ahead	proceed
go back on	fail to do
go by (time)	pass
go for	(i) attack
	(ii) try to get something
	(iii) choose
go into	(i) enter
	(ii) explain in detail
go off	explode
go over	repeat something in order to learn it
go through	experience something bad
go through with	finish something one has begun
go up	rise in value or price
go with	accompany

H

hand in	submit
hand out	distribute
hand over	surrender
hang around	wait, doing nothing
head back	return
head for	go towards
hold on	(i) wait or pause
	(ii) hold something firmly
hold out	refuse to give in
hold up	(i) remain strong
	(ii) delay

Phrasal Verb	Meaning(s)
K	
keep away from	avoid
keep off	stay at a distance
keep on	continue to do something
keep out	remain outside
keep up	maintain
knock off	stop work
knock out	make unconscious
L	
laugh at	scorn
laugh off	pretend that something is not as serious as it really is by laughing about it
lay out	(i) spread in an orderly way
	(ii) hit
leave out	omit
let off	(i) cause to explode
	(ii) allow to escape
let on	reveal a secret
look back on	remember something from one's past
look for	seek
look into	investigate
look on	watch
look out	pay attention or be careful
look up	search for
look up to	admire
look upon	regard
M	
make for	go towards
make out	(i) understand
	(ii) manage to see
	(iii) fill out (a bill or a check)
make up	(i) invent
	(ii) end a quarrel
	(iii) apply cosmetics
mess up	spoil or ruin
mistaken for	confuse someone with a different person
O	
open up	(i) talk honestly and freely
	(ii) start a business
own up	confess, admit
P	
part with	give something to someone else
pass away	die

Phrasal Verb	Meaning(s)
pass out	faint
point out	(i) show
	(ii) draw attention to
pull apart	separate people from a fight
pull through	(i) recover from illness
	(ii) succeed in avoiding difficulties or dangers
pull up	come to a stop
put down	(i) criticize someone
	(ii) suppress a revolution
put forward	suggest a plan or proposal
put off	(i) postpone
	(ii) take someone's attention away
put out	extinguish
put up	(i) stay
	(ii) erect
	(iii) hang or mount
put up with	bear or tolerate

R

Phrasal Verb	Meaning(s)
ring up	make a telephone call
run across	meet (someone) or find (something) by chance
run down	drive against so as to knock down
run into	meet by chance
run out of	have no more supply of
run over	(i) knock down and drive over (by a vehicle)
	(ii) rehearse or practice
	(iii) think about something
run up against	meet an obstacle

S

Phrasal Verb	Meaning(s)
see about	deal with
see to	deal with
set aside	reserve
set out	start a journey
set up	start or establish
set upon	attack with violence
settle down	(i) become calm or quiet
	(ii) begin a normal, stable life
settle up	pay one's debts
show off	boast
show up	arrive at a place
sit in for	take the place of somebody else at a meeting, discussion, etc.
size up	judge a person or situation

Phrasal Verb	Meaning(s)
sort out	separate
spark off	cause the start of
speak out	speak freely
speak up	speak audibly
spur on	encourage (someone) to try harder
stand by	(i) support
	(ii) wait
stand for	represent
stand out	be seen clearly
stand up for	support, defend
step down	leave one's official post
step in	intervene
stick to	never change

T

tail off	become gradually smaller or weaker
take after	resemble or look like
take away	remove someone or something
take back	admit that one was wrong to say something
take down	(i) write something down
	(ii) dismantle
take in	(i) deceive
	(ii) let someone stay in your house
take off	(i) begin to fly
	(ii) remove
	(iii) suddenly start being successful
take on	undertake
take over	take control of
take to	start to like
take up	(i) occupy
	(ii) start something new
taken aback	be surprised
talk back	answer someone in authority in a rude way
talk over	discuss or consider
tell off	rebuke
think over	consider carefully
throw up	vomit
touch on	talk briefly about
tuck away	eat heartily
turn down	reject
turn out (to be)	come to be
turn over to	(i) give control to
	(ii) hand to the police

Phrasal Verb	Meaning(s)
turn to	(i) ask for help
	(ii) get advice from
turn up	(i) come or arrive
	(ii) be found (especially by chance)
	(iii) happen
try out	test

V vouch for — say that someone is honest and has good character

W

wear out	exhaust
win back	regain
win over	get someone's support
wind up	bring to an end
wipe out	get rid of something completely
wither away	fade, die
work out	solve

4: SIMILES

as active as quicksilver
as agile as a monkey
as angry as a bull
as audacious as the day
as awkward as a cow on ice

as bad as a blight
as bald as an egg
as bare as a stone
as beautiful as the rainbow
as big as an elephant
as black as soot
as blank as an empty bottle
as blind as a bat
as bold as brass
as boundless as the ocean
as brave as a lion
as brief as a dream
as bright as the sun
as buoyant as wings
as busy as a bee

as calm as a cat
as candid as mirrors
as careless as the wind
as changeable as the weather
as cheap as dirt
as cheery as a sunbeam
as clean as a whistle
as clear as a bell
as clumsy as a bear
as cold as ice
as complacent as a cat
as confident as Hercules
as conscientious as a dog
as contagious as a yawn
as cool as cucumber
as countless as the sand
as crooked as a corkscrew
as cruel as death
as cunning as a fox

as dangerous as machine guns
as dark as a dungeon
as dead as wood
as deep as the sea
as devoted as a mother
as difficult as a Greek puzzle
as distant as the horizon
as dry as a bone

as eager as a beaver
as easy as ABC
as empty as space

as fair as the morn
as far apart as the poles
as fast as a deer
as feeble as a child
as flat as a pancake
as fickle as the weather
as fierce as a lion
as fit as a fiddle
as fresh as a daisy

as gentle as a lamb
as gloomy as the night
as good as gold
as graceful as a swan
as greedy as a hog

as hairy as a spider
as happy as a lark
as hard as iron
as heavy as lead

as immense as the sea
as industrious as a beaver

as joyful as a fly

as keen as a razor

as lasting as the pyramids
as light as a feather
as lively as a cricket

as meek as a lamb

as nervous as a mouse
as nimble as a lizard

as persistent as a mosquito
as playful as a kitten
as poor as a church mouse

as quarrelsome as the weasel
as quick as lightning

as red as a cherry
as rosy as a bride
as round as a barrel
as rude as a bear

as selfish as a fox
as slippery as an eel
as slow as a snail
as still as a statue
as stubborn as a mule
as sturdy as an oak
as swift as a hare

as tall as a giant
as thick as thieves
as timid as a mouse
as tough as leather

as ugly as a scarecrow

as vain as a peacock

as wet as a fish

like a bashful schoolgirl
like a faithful old dog
like a fish out of water
like a hungry wolf
like a monster
like a ponderous elephant
like a tenacious bulldog
like sardines in a can
like Siamese twins
like two peas in a pod

5: IDIOMS

Idiom		Meaning
a black sheep	:	someone who is regarded as a disgrace to the family or group
a bolt out of the blue	:	something that happens unexpectedly
a bull in a china shop	:	a very clumsy person
a chip off the old block	:	a son who is like his father
a close shave	:	a narrow escape
a cock and bull story	:	a silly and incredible story
a greenhorn	:	someone new and inexperienced
a pain in the neck	:	somebody who is annoying or tiresome
a rolling stone	:	a person who moves from one job or residence to another
a stone's throw	:	a very short distance
a tall story / tale	:	a story / tale that is hard to believe
a wet blanket	:	someone who tries to spoil other people's fun
a white lie	:	a lie one tells in order to avoid hurting someone
across the board	:	happening to people at all levels and in every area
add fuel to fire	:	make a bad situation even worse
alike as two peas	:	similar to each other
all and sundry	:	everyone, not just a selected few
all ears	:	to be attentive
an old hand	:	someone with a lot of experience
at one's fingertips	:	to know thoroughly
at the eleventh hour	:	at the last moment
bad blood	:	feelings of hatred between people because of past quarrels
be like a fish out of water	:	to feel awkward because of the situation in which one is placed
bite the bullet	:	to face up to something unpleasant

Idiom		Meaning
blow one's own trumpet	:	boast about oneself
break the ice	:	to make people who have not met before feel more relaxed so that they are willing to talk to each other
building castles in the air	:	daydreaming
burning the midnight oil	:	to work or study until late at night
bury the hatchet	:	agree to stop quarreling and become friends again
by hook or by crook	:	by fair means or by foul means
by leaps and bounds	:	very much, very quickly
by trial and error	:	to test different methods of doing something in order to find the best method
catch someone red-handed	:	to catch someone at the moment when he is doing something wrong
child's play	:	a very easy job or task
cry wolf	:	to appeal for help unnecessarily
dead broke	:	having no money at all
donkey's years	:	a very long time
eat one's words	:	to admit what one said was wrong
face the music	:	to accept the punishment
face to face	:	very close and in front of
follow someone's footsteps	:	to do the same job as someone else who did it before you
follow suit	:	to act in the same way as someone did previously
forty winks	:	a very short sleep
give someone the cold shoulder	:	to make someone feel unwelcome
give the green light	:	to give (someone) the permission to do something
hard of hearing	:	almost deaf
has a sweet tooth	:	likes to eat sweet things

Idiom		Meaning
in black and white	:	write it down on paper
in cold blood	:	deliberately and calmly
in the nick of time	:	only just in time
in the same boat	:	in the same difficult situation
in the red	:	owe more money than one has
Jack-of-all-trades	:	someone who can do many things, but is not skilled in any one of them
keep one's fingers crossed	:	to hope that something will be successful
keep the ball rolling	:	to keep things going
kick the bucket	:	to die
kill two birds with one stone	:	to achieve two aims from one action
like a bear with a sore head	:	to be very bad-tempered
live from hand to mouth	:	just able to survive with no savings
make a beeline for	:	to go quickly and directly towards someone or something
make a clean breast of	:	to confess in full
mind one's P's and Q's	:	to be careful how one behaves
miss the boat	:	to lose an opportunity
make heads or tails of something	:	make sense of something
no laughing matter	:	a serious matter
once in a blue moon	:	very rarely
out of the question	:	not possible or allowed
pour cold water on (someone)	:	to make someone feel discouraged
pull one's socks up	:	to make an effort to improve one's work
put on airs	:	to behave in a way that makes one seem more important than other people
put one's foot down	:	to be firm

Idiom		Meaning
raining cats and dogs	:	raining very hard
see eye to eye	:	to have the same point of view
see red	:	to lose one's temper
show one's true colors	:	to reveal one's real character
smell a rat	:	to suspect that something is wrong
the lion's share	:	the largest part
to be chicken-hearted	:	to be weak and cowardly
to be on cloud nine	:	to be extremely happy
to be up to the mark	:	to be up to a certain standard
to bear in mind	:	to remember
to beat around the bush	:	to talk in a roundabout way
to carry weight	:	to be important
to cry over spilt milk	:	to be upset over something about which nothing can be done
to drop someone a line	:	to write a letter to someone
to feel run-down	:	to feel unwell
to fly into a rage	:	to become angry suddenly
to foot the bill	:	to pay the bill
to get into hot water	:	to get into serious trouble
to have a big mouth	:	not being able to keep secrets
to have a green thumb	:	to be good at making plants grow
to hit the nail on the head	:	to come to the right conclusion
to hold one's tongue	:	to keep quiet
to keep a person at arm's length	:	to avoid being too familiar with a person
to keep an eye on	:	to watch carefully
to keep in touch	:	to keep in contact
to learn by heart	:	to memorize
to leave no stone unturned	:	to try one's hardest
to lend an ear	:	to listen to someone
to lend a hand	:	to help
to look daggers at	:	to look angrily at someone
to lose heart	:	to feel discouraged

Idiom	Meaning
to make a mountain out of a molehill	: to exaggerate
to make ends meet	: to spend within one's income
to mind one's own business	: to concern oneself with one's own affairs
to pass the hat round	: to collect donations
to pass with flying colors	: to do very well in a test
to pick and choose	: to choose very carefully
to rain cats and dogs	: to rain very heavily
to receive with open arms	: to welcome cordially
to save for a rainy day	: to save for a time when money is needed
to shed crocodile tears	: to shed false tears
to show the white flag	: to surrender
to strike while the iron is hot	: to seize the opportunity when it comes
to take someone under one's wing	: to help and protect someone who is younger or has less experience
to take to one's heels	: to run away at great speed
to turn a blind eye to	: to pretend not to see (something)
to turn a deaf ear to	: to deliberately ignore
to turn over a new leaf	: to change one's conduct for the better
to turn tail	: to run away
to turn turtle	: to turn upside down
to walk on air	: to be extremely happy
under one's nose	: to not notice something even though it is obviously happening right in front of one

6: PROVERBS

Proverb	Meaning
A bad workman blames his tools	An inefficient worker will always complain about the quality of his tools.
A fool and his money are soon parted	A foolish person easily squanders his money.
A light purse makes a heavy heart	We cannot be cheerful when we are faced with financial difficulties.
A friend in need is a friend indeed	A friend who helps you when you need it is a true friend.
A rolling stone gathers no moss	Someone who doesn't settle down cannot have real friendships or succeed in his life.
A stitch in time saves nine	It is better to deal with a problem early than to wait until it gets worse.
Actions speak louder than words	What a person does matters more than what he says.
All that glitters is not gold	Appearances are often deceptive.
All work and no play makes Jack a dull boy	We should not be constantly working, but should also take time to relax and pursue other activities.
All's well that ends well	If the final result is good, earlier setbacks no longer matter.
As you make your bed so you must lie in it	One must accept the bad results of his action.
Bad news travels fast	News such as accidents, deaths, illness, etc. are spread much more quickly.
Beauty is in the eye of the beholder	Different people have different opinions about what is beautiful.
Beggars cannot be choosers	When one has no money and no power to choose, he has to accept whatever is available.
Better late than never	Even if something happens late, it is better than not happening at all.

Proverb		Meaning
Birds of a feather flock together	:	People with similar characteristics, interests and beliefs tend to come together in groups.
Blood is thicker than water	:	Family ties are stronger than other relationships.
Books and friends should be few but good	:	Having a few good friends whom you can rely on is all that matters.
Born with a silver spoon in your mouth	:	A person who is born into a wealthy family.
Charity begins at home	:	One should help his own family, country, etc. before he helps other people.
Clothes do not make the man	:	It is a man's character that really counts, not what he wears.
Curiosity killed the cat	:	Asking questions about or interfering in what does not concern you can be dangerous.
Deeds are better than words	:	Helping someone by actions is better than just talking about the problem and giving advice, encouragement, etc.
Don't count your chickens before they are hatched	:	Do not assume the outcome until it actually happens.
Don't cry over spilled milk	:	It is a waste of time feeling sorry about an earlier mistake that cannot be changed.
Don't judge a book by its cover	:	One should not form an opinion of someone or something based on outward appearance.
Don't put all your eggs in one basket	:	Do not risk all your money, time, etc. on one single opportunity.
Easier said than done	:	Saying something is easier than actually doing it.
East or west, home is best	:	Ultimately, no matter where you go, there is no place like home.
Empty vessels make the most noise	:	People who are noisy and talkative are usually those who lack intelligence or sense.

Proverb	Meaning
Every cloud has a silver lining	: No matter how difficult or unpleasant a situation may be, it has some advantages.
Every dog has its day	: Every person will, at some time in his life, be successful.
Every man is the architect of his own fortune	: Life is what you make it out to be.
Good things come in small packages	: Something big does not necessarily mean that it is good.
Half a loaf is better than no bread	: We should be thankful for what we receive, even when it is not as much as we have hoped for.
More haste, less speed	: It is useless to do something too hastily as this often produces shoddy work that will need to be redone.
He who wills the end wills the means	: By being determined to do something, you will be able to find a way.
Honesty is the best policy	: It is best to be honest in all our dealings.
Hunger is the best sauce	: When you are hungry, any food would taste delicious.
Kill two birds with one stone	: You achieve two things with one action.
Let bygones be bygones	: We should forgive and forget unpleasant things that are in the past.
Let sleeping dogs lie	: Do not do anything that will stir up unnecessary trouble.
Look before you leap	: It is wise to think about possible dangers or difficulties before doing something.
Make hay while the sun shines	: One should act when conditions are favorable.
Many hands make light work	: Sharing work makes doing it much easier.
Never say die	: Never give up.
Nobody is perfect	: Everyone has made mistakes in their lives.

Proverb		Meaning
Once bitten, twice shy	:	If one has failed or been hurt once, he will be very careful next time.
One good turn deserves another	:	If someone does something nice for you, you should do likewise.
One man's meat is another man's poison	:	One person may like what another hates.
Out of sight, out of mind	:	We cease to think about anything that can no longer be seen.
Practice makes perfect	:	Only by doing something again and again will you become skilled at it.
Prevention is better than cure	:	It is wiser to prevent a trouble from happening than to let it happen and repair the damage later.
Rome was not built in a day	:	It takes time, patience and hard work to accomplish a difficult or important task.
Still waters run deep	:	A quiet person may have very strong feelings or know a lot.
The early bird catches the worm	:	One can miss an opportunity by not acting promptly.
The pot should not call the kettle black	:	One should not criticize someone for a fault that he also has.
Tomorrow is another day	:	There will be another opportunity to do something.
Too many cooks spoil the broth	:	A job will be mismanaged if too many people try to do it together.
Two heads are better than one	:	Two people may be able to solve a problem that one person cannot.
Two wrongs do not make a right	:	Taking revenge on a person who harms you will not make a situation right or fair.
Waste not, want not	:	Do not waste anything as you may need it in the future.
Where there's a will, there's a way	:	With determination, you can find a way of doing something.

NOTES

NOTES

NOTES